ALL ABOUT
SAGUAROS

FACTS | LORE | PHOTOS

BY LEO W. BANKS | PHOTOGRAPHS BY ARIZONA HIGHWAYS CONTRIBUTORS

Author LEO W. BANKS
Book Designer KRIS SOTELO
Photography Editor PETER ENSENBERGER
Book Editor BOB ALBANO
Copy Editor EVELYN HOWELL
Map and Illustrations KEVIN KIBSEY

Library of Congress Control Number: 2008927790
ISBN: 978-1-932082-91-3
First Printing: 2008. Printed in China

Published by the Book Division of *Arizona Highways* magazine,
a monthly publication of the Arizona Department of Transportation,
2039 West Lewis Avenue, Phoenix, Arizona 85009.
Telephone: (602) 712-2200
Web site: www.arizonahighways.com

Publisher WIN HOLDEN
Editor ROBERT STIEVE
Books Managing Editor BOB ALBANO
Associate Editor EVELYN HOWELL
Art Director BARBARA DENNEY
Director of Photography PETER ENSENBERGER
Production Director MICHAEL BIANCHI
Production Assistants ANNETTE PHARES, DIANA BENZEL-RICE,
        RONDA JOHNSON

ARIZONA HIGHWAYS

FRONT COVER Saguaro National Park (shown is the west or Tucson Mountains unit) protects
and displays some of the Sonoran Desert's finest stands of saguaro cactus. The scene vividly
illustrates that a bajada — the usually rocky terrain sloping between a mountain base and a
plain — provides ideal habitat for cactus plants. George H.H. Huey

PREVIOUS PAGE A saguaro's ribs swell and shrink in relation to the recent amount of water it
has absorbed. George Stocking

BACK COVER Although saguaros usually grow in stands, there are locations, such as this one
in the Sierra Ancha Wilderness east of Phoenix, where only a few inhabit an area along with a
variety of other desert vegetation. Tom Vezo

CONTENTS

A saguaro's blossoming cycle occurs in May and June, but not until the cactus is at least 50 years old and 7 to 8 feet tall. The flowering, quickly followed by fruiting, occurs on a timetable accommodating hungry creatures and taking advantage of the desert's summer rains. Tom Vezo

PORTFOLIO

People consider the saguaro cactus as the monarch of the Sonoran Desert. In global terms, the saguaro is rare. The only place (with a few minor exceptions) where it grows is the Sonoran Desert. In turn, the Sonoran Desert is confined to portions of southern and central Arizona and northwestern Mexico.

Indeed, people deem saguaros as possessing personalities, character, and communication skills. Photographs in this portfolio document that point, showing the seemingly endless number of the saguaro's poses and settings.

So, slowly turn the pages of this portfolio, savor the saguaro's beauty, and appreciate its importance to animals and the desert.

We open the portfolio with an image made by Jack Dykinga showing fiery colors birthed by an eruption of a volcano on Mount Pinatubo on the island of Luzon in the Philippines.

Jack Dykinga

LEFT Three saguaros punctuate a community of plants in the Sierra Ancha Wilderness, a remote, rugged region east of Phoenix. Tom Vezo

ABOVE A crested saguaro may be the botanical world's version of a cult figure. Researchers believe that fewer than 700 crested saguaros exist, this one in the Organ Pipe Cactus National Monument in southwestern Arizona. The crest results from a mutation. Paul Gill

FAR LEFT With a dusting of snow on the tips of their arms and their surroundings coated in white, these saguaros resemble sentinels in a ghostly scene in the Tucson area's Santa Catalina Mountains. C.K. Lorenz

ABOVE Even when only its skeleton remains, a saguaro serves many roles — this one as a high perch for a Cooper's hawk searching for prey. Tom Vezo

LEFT The saguaro cactuses and this mule deer doe are ideally suited to survive in the Sonoran Desert. If the deer can't locate water, it might nibble into a cactus to extract moisture. G.C. Kelley

FAR LEFT Weather elements have separated the saguaro's ribs into willow-like strands projecting an artistic foreground for this scene in the Sonoran Desert National Monument below the Sand Tank Mountains. Jack Dykinga

ABOVE This flatland stretch in the Ironwood National Monument draws the right amount of moisture, sunshine, and protection for saguaros. Newman Peak lies in the background. Laurence Parent

LEFT Although javelinas don't rely on saguaros for food, this one seems to be gnawing on the ribs. Perhaps, the peccary is scratching an itch or cleaning its teeth. Paul and Joyce Berquist

FAR LEFT A diversity of age exists among these saguaros. The several in the foreground are younger, not having grown arms. But their neighbors — perhaps parents — bear arms, putting them at least in the half-century-old class. The stand lies in Alamo Canyon, located in Organ Pipe Cactus National Monument. George Stocking

ABOVE Few scenes project the West more classically than this one. Jerry Jacka

LEFT During a very wet year, Roosevelt Lake in east-central Arizona rises to encircle a saguaro. Paul Gill

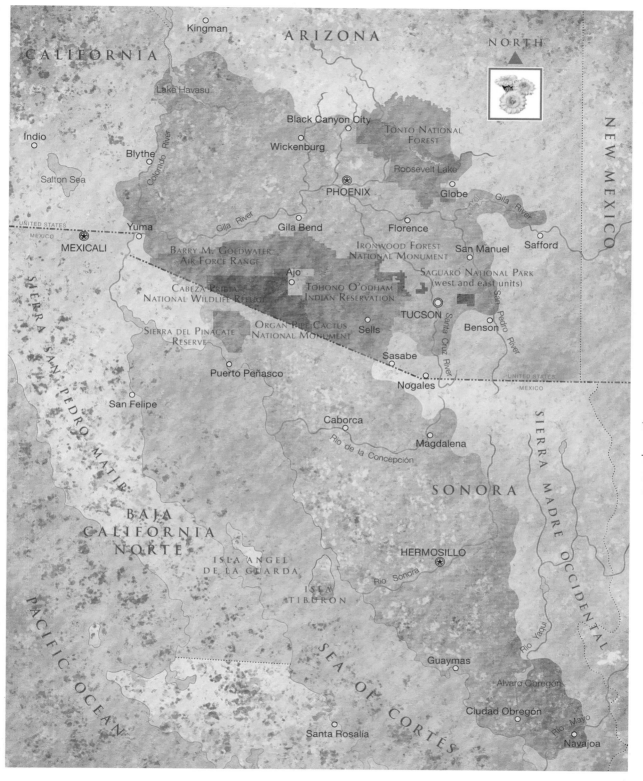

LEFT Saguaro flowers blossom in a precisely orchestrated sequence to satisfy the varying needs of birds and other creatures that feed on them. Jack Dykinga

ABOVE The green tint shows the saguaro's range, stretching from western Sonora, Mexico, to an area about 30 miles south of Kingman, Arizona. Kevin Kibsey

THE BASICS

What the Saguaro Means to Us

The saguaro cactus is everywhere, not just on the landscape of southern and central Arizona, but also in our hearts and minds.

From man's first recorded encounters with this so-called monarch of the Sonoran Desert, we have viewed it as more than a plant.

It's one of us, not just living, but alive with its own personality, character, and means of communicating.

Tohono O'odham Indians, whose homeland encompasses much of the plant's geographic range, consider saguaros people and ostracize anyone who would bring them harm.

The ethnobotanist Gary Nabhan tells the Tohono O'odham story of a boy, unable to remove fruit from a saguaro with the traditional pole, asking an O'odham woman if he could throw rocks at it instead. She sternly tells him no.

"If you hit them in the head with rocks, you could kill them," she says. "You don't do anything to hurt them. They are Indians."

When the Spanish explored what is now the American Southwest in the mid-1500s, encountering the saguaro for the first time, their correspondents referred to an area near present-day downtown Tucson as "the land of the marching giants."

From that we can assume they were impressed. The Spanish didn't just compare saguaros to people; they made them huge, stately, and powerful people, like chieftains lording over their terrain.

Five centuries later, we continue the tradition of seeing humanity in them.

One example is a 1964 essay by Joseph Wood Krutch, who made an admirable attempt at profiling the imposing plant.

He noted the variety of looks evident in a saguaro forest, with some of the branches rising almost vertically while others "first bend gracefully down before rising in a beautiful curve."

Krutch continued: "I have heard the saguaro's character described in a dozen different ways, but the most surprising (though not wholly inappropriate)

PRECEDING PANEL, PAGE 16 Although freezing weather damaged this gnarled saguaro, it continues to produce new limbs. The cactus is located in the Sonoran Desert National Monument, a 487,000-acre preserve administered by the federal Bureau of Land Management southwest of Phoenix. Jack Dykinga

LEFT This stand of stately saguaros dominates a desert scene in the Cabeza Prieta National Wildlife Refuge along El Camino del Diablo (the Devil's Road) in southwestern Arizona. George Stocking

TOP Mature saguaros produce flowers from late April into June. After the flowers progress into fruit, their seeds are spread by a variety of creatures, including birds and coyotes. C.K. Lorenz

ABOVE The number of arms on this healthy saguaro in the Usery Mountain Regional Park east of Phoenix indicates it's probably at or beyond the century mark in age. Saguaros usually begin growing arms when they are from 50 to 70 years old. Wes Johnson

was in the remark of a young woman visitor from New Zealand who said, 'I think they are very witty.'

"Indeed, there is a sort of fanciful cleverness or wit in the way the saguaro handles its huge bulk with graceful variety."

Those who've never quite associated cleverness with a plant might think twice about that. But that's okay. Everyone sees in the saguaro what they want to see.

Browse Arizona business directories and notice how many businesses use the word "saguaro" in their titles.

Some don't fit at all. What's the connection, for example, between saguaros and dermatology? Or drywall?

Saguaros and acupuncture? Now that works. Back into those sharp spines and you'll get the point.

The city of Tucson uses the saguaro on its official seal, but that's only the beginning of its exposure in southern Arizona. It's also on the Arizona state quarter, and the blossom is Arizona's state flower.

Desert residents can't escape the big lug. Drivers see it standing at the roadside, on medians, and on our horizons, as well as on bumper stickers that offer the greeting, "Saguaro You Today?"

But its admirers range across the United States, and some don't take kindly to anyone who might harm their favorite succulent.

An offbeat Texas musical group, the Austin Lounge Lizards, performs a popular song called *Saguaro*. It harkens back to a 1982 incident in which David Grundman, a 24-year-old Arizona man, used a giant saguaro for target practice. The lyrics of *Saguaro* describe what happened:

> *His finger twitched, he made his move,*
> *He drew, his guns did bark,*
> *And echoed with his laughter,*
> *As the bullets hit their mark.*
>
> *Now the mighty cactus trembled,*
> *Then came that warning sound.*
> *One mighty arm of justice*
> *Came hurtling toward the ground.*
>
> *The gunman staggered backward,*
> *He whimpered and he cried.*
> *The saguaro ... crushed him like a bug,*
> *And David Grundman died.*

LEFT In their natural habitat, such as this one in the Superstition Mountains east of Phoenix, saguaros present a stately appearance, accentuating a field laced with Mexican goldpoppies and scalloped phacelia. Jack Dykinga

TOP AND ABOVE Despite a dignified presence in nature, the saguaro sometimes is cast into burlesque roles, such as the decoration for an automobile antenna and the desert-style Santa in a Phoenix yard. Edward McCain and Dianne Dietrich Leis

The song tells a true story, and we don't have to guess where the sympathies of the Lizards lie.

If the Grundman incident conjures images of the American frontier, that's appropriate. Even though it grows primarily in the Sonoran Desert (see map on page 15), the saguaro has become an all-purpose symbol for everything wild and Western.

The 1988 Miss USA Pageant, for example, used a saguaro as a prop in an Old West song and dance routine. Television beamed this entertainment across the world from El Paso.

There's Texas again. Except for Arizona, that state seems to produce more saguaro admirers than any other, even though the cactus doesn't grow there.

In fact, the nearest one is some 200 miles to the west.

But that's not unusual. Saguaros don't grow in a lot of places where they're used as symbols, and in some places where you do see them, they're not really there.

Larson Camouflage, a Tucson-based company, builds fiberglass cell phone towers disguised as saguaros.

These fake cactuses sometimes stand alongside the real thing, fooling everyone, even the birds, as they bounce signals around the world.

Even disguised, the saguaro grabs our attention for good reason. It's an amazing plant. No one can look at one for the first time and look away.

In March of 1981, Joe McAuliffe was a graduate student sleeping in the back of a van as it rolled down Interstate 17 between Flagstaff and Phoenix.

Below Black Canyon City, the Nebraska native awoke and peered out the window, seeing the Sonoran Desert for the first time. He was too awed to yawn.

Now director of research at the Desert Botanical Garden in Phoenix, McAuliffe stayed in that van until it reached Organ Pipe Cactus National Monument, along the Mexican border in southwest Arizona.

His awe grew as he walked around that remarkable desert place.

"I heard cactus wrens and saw ocotillo branches waving in the wind and these peculiar, green-barked paloverde trees," McAuliffe says. "The plants were spaced so you could walk among them as if you were in some Japanese Zen garden. I'd stepped into a different world. It was magical."

But the saguaro really captured his eye.

"From the time I first saw this plant, I knew I wanted to study it," McAuliffe says. "Everybody does. Everybody wants to get close to it. Tourists want to have their picture taken with it. The saguaro is a charismatic beast for sure."

LEFT A mixture of relatively young and old saguaros punctuate a bajada flowing into a flat plain in the west unit of Saguaro National Park near Tucson. Sharing the scene are teddy bear cholla, brittlebush, and ocotillo. George H.H. Huey

TOP The Desert Botanical Garden in east Phoenix is a popular attraction featuring saguaro cactuses and many other desert plants. Morey K. Milbradt

ABOVE The cactus wren, Arizona's state bird, favors the cactus as a nest-building site because the thorns help protect the bird from predators. Sometimes, wrens take up residence in holes bored in saguaros by woodpeckers. Bruce D. Taubert

Basic Facts About the Saguaro

The attraction begins, as attraction often does, with physical appearance.

The bigger saguaros grow 25 to 35 feet tall, and a few shoot up to 45 feet or more. The average saguaro hangs around between 125 and 175 years — with great-grandpappies making it well past 200 years.

Some perspective: If you visit a cactus forest in Arizona, you could easily find yourself standing beside a thriving plant that also was alive in 1807, when Thomas Jefferson was president and the great poet Henry Wadsworth Longfellow was still an infant in his mother's blankets in Portland, Maine.

One fact always proves memorable to first-time desert visitors: the length of time the saguaro takes to grow its first arm. Think of the saguaro as a spindle — narrow at the base, broader higher up, then narrow again on up to its peak. Although it varies from region to region, the plant's first arms often appear just above the point of its greatest diameter, usually about the 7-foot mark.

But the arms don't show up for at least 50 years, more likely showing around 70.

A multiarmed saguaro looks proud, even theatrical, with its arms curling toward the sky in splendor.

If this comes across as a boastful pose, it's well deserved. After all, a 35-foot-tall plant with six or seven arms easily can weigh 7½ tons. That's 14,000 pounds, as much as two Hummers carrying two families of four with dogs, camping gear, and a few in-laws tossed in.

And it's 95 to 96 percent water, which is odd, considering that it grows in a desert. But the Sonoran Desert is one of the wettest deserts in North America, and that precipitation helps the saguaro keep its foothold here.

The plant's range stretches throughout southern Arizona and western Sonora, Mexico.

On the north, saguaros dot the landscape all the way up to Mohave County, stopping about 30 miles south of Kingman.

LEFT, TOP AND BOTTOM Saguaros seem to present themselves in their best light when the sun is low in the sky — around dawn and in the late afternoon or early evening. These mature plants are located in the Organ Pipe Cactus National Monument in southwestern Arizona. The rocky framing is provided by the Ajo Mountains.
Randy Prentice and Les David Manevitz

RIGHT With five mature arms and a few that are developing, this saguaro probably inhabited the Superstition Mountains east of Phoenix at about the time that Jacob Waltz, of the famed "Lost Dutchman Mine," was poking around them in search of gold. Morey K. Milbradt

On the east, they begin on the Gila River, not far from Safford in Markham Canyon. From there they head up the San Pedro River toward Benson, skirting the eastern edge of the Sonoran Desert, with a few outliers around Nogales.

Other than Arizona, California is the only U.S. state that can boast having saguaros. They don't grow in New Mexico, Texas, Colorado, or Utah.

But the California population numbers barely a hundred or so. They stand in the Chocolate, Whipple, and Picacho mountains on the California side of the Colorado River. These saguaros form the western border of the plant's range, and a hill called Cerro Masiaca, near the city of Navajoa in Sonora, Mexico, forms the southern border.

Across the Sonoran Desert's 120,000 square miles (or 76,800,000 acres), saguaros vary widely in how and where they grow and even how they look.

Western saguaros usually don't have arms and are pretty thin, due to a lack of water. The deserts around Yuma, near the California-Arizona border, draw the lowest rainfall of any within the saguaro range, fewer than 3 inches per year.

The densest populations of saguaros, and the largest specimens, grow around the Santa Catalina, Rincon, and Tucson mountain ranges on the north, east, and west ends of the Tucson valley.

But in the far northern and eastern portions of its range, cold weather thins out saguaro stands and restricts them to small areas with favorable growing conditions.

If the long-term climate were to change significantly, the location of saguaros on the landscape would change with it.

A warmer climate might send saguaros scampering higher up mountainsides.

A decrease in summer rain might shift their western margin eastward, eliminating saguaros from California entirely.

Drainages, such as this one in the Sierra Ancha Wilderness northeast of Phoenix, provide growing conditions for both saguaros and deciduous plants. Tom Vezo

FAR LEFT After a summer rain storm, water fills a normally dry wash in the east unit of Saguaro National Park near Tucson. C.K. Lorenz

LEFT Can anything seem more incongruous than desert vegetation dusted by snow? It's not a common occurrence, but it happens as this scene in the Santa Catalina Mountains north of Tucson verifies. Jack Dykinga

Big changes have happened before.

Here's a remarkable fact to consider: At one time, no saguaros stood anywhere in Tucson. They simply didn't exist there.

But human beings were there, working, planting, living and dying in an environment that was completely different from what it is today, without our beloved symbol.

What sparked the saguaro's arrival?

By the end of the Pleistocene epoch 11,500 years ago, the climate had moderated from icy cold to dry and warm, and the change eventually opened the door to new plant life, including the saguaro.

It became a fixture on southern Arizona's landscape only 10,000 years ago.

If, magically, we had a time-lapse camera to show the evolution of the saguaro from the time of its appearance to the present, we'd see how vegetative patterns have come and gone as the climate has continued to shift and how saguaros have met and overcome those changes.

"It's a rough world, and the saguaros that are out there now are survivors," says Matt Johnson, program manager and curator of the University of Arizona's Desert Legume Program. "They're tough customers that have adapted very well over the millennia to life here in the Sonoran Desert. It's what they're best at."

Tough as they might be on the surface, deep down saguaros are tender souls and real long shots to survive.

Consider that in its reproductive lifespan, the average saguaro might produce 40 million seeds.

In a saguaro forest that maintains a consistent population over time, only one of those seeds will survive to become a mature saguaro.

These are very long odds for life.

LIFETIME

Germination of the Seeds

To germinate, the saguaro seed needs favorable conditions in a favorable year, and time is of the essence.

"Its lifespan is so short compared with, say, a mesquite seed," says Ray Turner, a retired research botanist for the U.S. Geological Survey. He has been a leading saguaro researcher for more than 50 years.

"The [mesquite seed] can survive for years. But a saguaro seed will last only a few months in the soil bank. If the right conditions for germination don't occur in that short period of time, it's all over for that year."

The seedlings that do survive sprout in the protective shadow of a nurse plant, such as a paloverde, ironwood, or mesquite tree. The nurse doesn't have to be a tree, but could be something as small as bursage brush or a simple clump of grass.

The ground beneath these nurse plants holds more moisture and more nutrients, mostly from decaying leaves and branches, and above all it's shady.

In the full sun, a baby saguaro bakes and dies. Under a nurse tree, where it might be 20° cooler, it lives.

Nurse trees also provide warmth in winter.

The temperature underneath a paloverde might be three or four degrees higher than in the open air 5 feet away, and those few degrees can make the difference between survival and death on the coldest winter nights.

But nurse plants are important for another reason having to do with one of Nature's immutable laws — if there's something good to eat, an animal will come along and eat it.

A 3-month-old saguaro seedling is nothing more than a little green blob of jelly with tiny hair-like spines.

It's defenseless and a terrific snack for birds, packrats, even caterpillars.

If the seedling is invisible, however, hidden beneath the branches of a mesquite, it can escape these hungry critters.

PRECEDING PANEL, PAGE 30 Perhaps this flowering ironwood tree functioned as a nurse to the saguaro when it was but a few inches tall and unable to fend for itself. Eventually, the cactus might take over the spot it shares with the ironwood, causing its death. Bruce Griffin

LEFT This saguaro in the Sand Tank Mountains, southwest of Gila Bend, may have contributed to the demise of its neighboring tree. The decaying branches still afford the cactus some protection from animals that could harm it. Jack Dykinga

ABOVE Although it's smaller than the neighboring saguaro, the fishhook cactus has reached maturity while the saguaro is still a youngster, seemingly hiding out amid green foliage. Laurence Parent

But Mother Nature often rules with a heartless hand.

In time, after the saguaro has grown to self-sufficiency, it begins to compete with its nurse plant for water, in some cases causing the nurse's death.

The saguaro, though, usually has many decades of growth ahead.

First, it must survive the seedling stage, and in this effort moisture is critical.

The seedling has minimal water storage capacity, roughly equal to that of a grain of rice. It relies, particularly in its first summer, on a regular supply of rain.

Turner and research partner Betsy Pierson found that wherever scientists have seen a period of substantial saguaro regeneration — defined as an old population being replaced by successful seedlings — the reason was a moist climate.

This occurred from 1907 through 1959 in the Sierra del Pinacate Reserve in northern Sonora, Mexico,
and from 1915 through 1940 at Organ Pipe Cactus National Monument.

But good summer rains alone don't do the trick.

These have to be followed by winter rains to bring the seedlings along, as well as a good balance of shade and sunlight, which allows the plant to grow.

If drought follows the summer monsoons, or if the winter rains don't come in just the right amount, the seedling will likely die.

All of which means the young saguaro is quite demanding, requiring a conspiracy of conditions to live.

Up to 6 inches in height, the plant is still pretty vulnerable to the harsh desert environment.

But after it reaches a foot tall, and its spines are finally tough enough to deter predators, the saguaro has a good chance of living to a ripe old age.

Even then, it grows at its own glacial pace.

LEFT These two saguaros may have been a part of a regeneration flurry that permeated the Organ Pipe Cactus National Monument from 1915 through 1940. A moist climate is essential for such a burst of growth. The paloverde trees likely nursed the saguaros that now grow through the trees. The area also has been kind to chain fruit chollas near the saguaros and the poppies and globe mallow in the foreground. Bob Clemenz

ABOVE A saguaro's growth rate is proportionate to the amount of moisture it receives. These two lie in Pima Canyon, a natural drainage of the Santa Catalina Mountains north of Tucson. Randy Prentice

How a Seedling Grows

We're in a powerful hurry to get places and do things. But the saguaro, the personification of patience, just stands there, seeming to wonder what all the rush is about.

A seedling getting the right portions of shade and moisture might grow a measly quarter of an inch per year.

At a foot tall, the same plant might grow 1 to 2 inches per year, and at 8 feet tall, when the plant has substantially increased its water storage capacity, it really steps on the gas.

At this height, a saguaro can clock up to 8 or 9 inches of growth per year, with most of that coming in June, July, and August.

Moisture, again, is a key factor. In a dry year, even a healthy saguaro won't grow much at all.

That happens in the low deserts around Yuma and the Sea of Cortés, where annual rainfall might total only 3 inches.

In wetter portions of the eastern and northern Sonoran Desert, which get about 8 inches of rain per year, a saguaro can grow 1 inch its first year, and even reach a foot after a decade.

But the young saguaro has good reason for taking its time. It's busy establishing a root system, and most of its energy goes into this important work.

The saguaro has a spreading system of roots that forms roughly a circle around its base. They extend to a distance about equal to the height of the plant and in some cases two times beyond.

Most of these roots are shallow, in the top foot of soil, allowing easy access to oxygen and water. The most active roots lie so close to the surface that even a light rain can activate them.

Within six hours of rainfall, these roots grow fine hairs that allow them to take up available water.

At that critical task, the saguaro is a wonder of nature.

A few days after one heavy rain, a mature plant can absorb up to a ton of water.

TOP The regeneration cycle usually begins in May with the sprouting of flowers on the ends of saguaro arms and main trunk. But the timing of the cycle varies with elevation. G.C. Kelley

LEFT These saguaros, still guarded by their nurse, are too young to sprout flowers. Flowering begins at age 50 or 60. Paul and Joyce Berquist

On rare occasions, because it doesn't have a turnoff valve, the saguaro can actually absorb too much water, and the stem of the plant splits open.

Otherwise, it grabs onto that water and holds on for dear life.

This fattening process is visible.

Look at a saguaro at the end of a dry June, then again four weeks later after the summer rains. The diameter of the plant's stem might have increased by 50 percent.

In 1959, the late scientist James Rodney Hastings, one of Turner's former research partners, used an ingenious method to determine exactly how much a saguaro can expand.

Working at the University of Arizona's Desert Laboratory on Tumamoc Hill in Tucson, he cleared the spines from circular areas around his test saguaros, then wrapped metal bands tightly around these cleared spaces.

The bands were spring-loaded to expand and contract, and rigged with recording gauges to give Hastings a continuous record of the expanding girth of the saguaros.

He found that after good rains, the circumference of one saguaro increased from 31 to 47 inches, a remarkable transformation made possible by its vertical pleats.

They're one of Nature's engineering marvels.

Prior to taking in the water, the stem is folded and pleated. Afterward, the pleats disappear and the stem is almost flat.

Think of a bear, fattening in the fall and going into hibernation in winter, when its respiration and heart rate slow.

The saguaro does something similar — it drinks in water during the summer rains and stores it beneath its waxy outer skin, away from the heat and sun, for use during lean times.

This water-storage system is one means by which the saguaro adapts to its desert environment.

Another is by saving its most important work for the night shift.

All plants have little pores — called stomates — through which they breathe. As a water-saving strategy, the saguaro, like other succulents, opens its stomates at night when it's cooler and closes them during the day.

In this way, the plant loses less water vapor.

The saguaro is essentially holding its breath during the hottest hours.

TOP A mixture of saguaro cactus and chuparosa is a common sight in the Organ Pipe Cactus National Monument in southwestern Arizona. Chuparosa blossoms are a favorite of hummingbirds; thus the plant sometimes is called the hummingbird bush. Randy Prentice

BOTTOM This desert community in the Rincon Mountain, or east, unit of Saguaro National Park includes a grouping of young saguaro cactuses protected by paloverde trees and, in the foreground, a barrel cactus and paperflowers. After the blooms of paperflowers dry, they cling to the plant, and when the wind blows, they rustle like paper being crumpled. Randy Prentice

It stores the carbon dioxide it takes in overnight and converts it to sugars in the light of the following day.

This photosynthetic process gives the plant the energy it needs to grow.

The spines are also crucial in its desert-survival plan.

On a young saguaro, the spines are actually thicker than those on an older one, and they provide critical shade.

Hard as it is to believe, those spines can keep a young saguaro as much as 70 percent in the shade.

And they continue working as the plant matures. The yellow-white spines at the tips of the arms protect that crucial area, the growth point, from radiation, cold, and heat.

Notice, too, the cottony-white substance at the base of the spines. These are glandular hairs that provide additional reflectivity and insulation.

But for pure evolutionary genius, nothing can match the saguaro's remarkable production of flowers, fruit, and edible seeds.

The plant's productive phase occurs once a year, in summer, and by the time it is done, this plant will have transformed itself into something for which it is rarely given credit — a generous and reliable food source, a veritable breadbasket of the Sonoran Desert.

TOP Fire has ravaged this saguaro, robbing it of protective spines that it needs to survive. Paul Gill

CENTER Spines provide a saguaro with shade from the desert sun, insulation from cold, and prevention of damage by browsing animals. Bruce Griffin

BOTTOM Reproductive parts of a saguaro flower include a stigma (resembling fingers) just below the petals and a slender style linking it to the ovary at the bottom. Kevin Kibsey

A Cactus in Bloom

Matt Johnson, program manager and curator of the Desert Legume Program at the University of Arizona (UA), jokes that the saguaro starts to think about reproducing about the same time most humans start to think of retirement.

It's true. The plant sports its first flowers at 50 to 60 years old.

It happens around May 1, although blooming might start a couple of weeks earlier in low elevations and two weeks later higher up.

The appearance of these trumpet-shaped, white and yellow beauties, which occurs when the plant is 7 to 8 feet tall, marks the start of a timeless rite of spring.

Those who understand the unique rhythms of the desert look forward to it. Those who know this special

A timeless rite of spring is beginning. As evening's darkness descends, the buds will open into flowers for one night only. The next day the flowers will die in the afternoon sun. Gill Kenny

place only from cliché, rumor, or windshield observation are surprised and delighted when they finally understand it.

A desert full of color and spring magic? How can this be? Isn't it a dry and lifeless landscape?

Tell that to the blooming saguaro.

Its flowers open late in the evening on the tips of the main stem and on the tips of its arms.

None stay around long. The same flower that blossoms in the cool of midnight will die in the sun late the following afternoon.

But within those few hours, the saguaro is a hub of activity, a Grand Central Station for hungry pollinators.

Bats arrive first, drawn by the flower's mother-of-pearl glow, so bright it's visible even under starlight.

But under moonlight, the flowers shine like fluorescent bulbs. These beacons attract the lesser long-nosed bat and the Mexican long-tongued bat to feed on its nectar and pollen.

Saguaro flowers produce that nectar in waves, according to Bill Peachey, park scientist at Colossal Cave Mountain Park in Tucson.

It peaks first about 10 P.M., after which production drops off at midnight; then it picks up again just before dawn.

TOP It's April, and this desert foothills scene north of Phoenix along Interstate 17 rejoices in the color of blooming paloverde trees and saguaro cactuses. Robert McDonald

LEFT The saguaro flower is about 3 inches wide and consists of clustered creamy white petals around yellow stamens on a 4-inch stem. The colors are not just for beauty — they attract hungry creatures, who will feast on nectar and pollen and at the same time pollinate the flowers. Joe Zinn

"What's interesting is that the saguaro produces for nighttime animals first, mainly nectar for bats and moths," says Peachey. "In the morning it produces nectar and pollen for bees and birds. But the saguaro's first target is bats."

In his studies, Peachey has found that bats do not feed on the flowers in flocks as originally thought. Modern night vision equipment has proven that it is done by bats making repeat trips to the same flower.

A bat will rise to a 400- or 500-foot elevation, and fly along until it targets the reflection of a shiny saguaro flower.

It goes into a choreographed routine, hesitating momentarily inches from the flower, then darting its tongue into and out of the flowers several times a second.

After that it falls away, stalls in midair again, like a diner taking a moment to savor the experience, then dives in once more.

These bats can fly 25 miles one way to feed.

By morning, the bats have finished their pollination work and moved on, making room for insects, birds, and especially bees.

One study found that bees are so efficient at harvesting pollen that virtually all of it is gone by 9 or 10 A.M.

Fruit and Housing for All

Once pollinated, the flowers become fruit. But the ripening process takes another two months, and in late June or early July, the green fruit breaks open, exposing its moist, crimson interior.

Amid this pulp is a storehouse of tiny seeds, each one black, round, and no larger than a poppy seed.

If the opening of the fruit made a sound, it would be like a dinner bell summoning all sorts of hungry

TOP LEFT By early morning, the saguaro's nectar and pollen suit the taste of a Bullock's oriole. Bruce D. Taubert

TOP RIGHT Curve-billed thrashers also like the taste of saguaro flowers in the morning. Bruce D. Taubert

ABOVE Bees, too, light on saguaro flowers to feed and pollinate. Saguaro flowers have more stamens (the yellow part) than any other cactus. Paul and Joyce Berquist

birds. They gather on blooming saguaro stems like football players at a buffet table. But there's plenty for everyone. Scientists estimate that a large adult saguaro produces 1 million seeds every five years.

Humans join the feast as well.

As they have for centuries, Tohono O'odham Indians gather in desert camps in summer to harvest the high-growing fruit with long poles, making it into jam, syrup, and summer drinks. The seeds can even be ground into flour to make saguaro bread. The fruit carries a faint flavor some liken to strawberry.

Within a few weeks, the fruit begins dropping to the ground, and that calls forth a new cadre of hungry critters.

"In July everything comes to feed on saguaro fruit," says Peachey. "It begins with bats, birds, and bees and goes to desert tortoises, javelinas, rabbits, squirrels, wood rats, coyotes, and foxes. That time of year, you'll find coyote and fox droppings that are solid saguaro seeds."

Because these seeds usually do not digest well, the animals disperse them throughout the desert in their droppings, a primary source of new germinations.

"The white-winged dove does most of the seed-spreading work," says Turner. "After eating the fruit, the dove flies to a mesquite branch, defecates, and the seeds fall right where they need to be, in the cool nourishing ground beneath the nurse tree."

This reproduction process — from flowering to fertilizing, from pollination to seed spreading — follows a tight schedule that the saguaro has honed to perfection over thousands of years. Because the seeds do not

FAR LEFT In June and July, the pollinated flowers become red, juicy fruit — a treat for birds; mammals such as rabbits, coyotes, and foxes; and humans. Wasson Peak in the Tucson Mountains west of the city lies in the background. Randy Prentice

TOP Dining on cactus fruit are a white-winged dove (left) and a house finch. The red on the finch is part of a male's natural coloring, not an indication that it's a sloppy eater. The fruit's seeds are not digested very well and will end up in soil when the creatures defecate. Bruce D. Taubert

ABOVE Dried petals loom over an opened fruit with its seeds imbedded in pulp. On the ribs are central spines, each with radial spines. Kevin Kibsey

germinate in winter, the plant's strategy is to have its fruit open and its seeds ready to spread before the first summer rains come in early July.

"The seed has to be on the ground and germinating as soon as possible, to grow as big as possible, before the summer rains stop," says Peachey. "There's not a lot of time. The seedlings most apt to survive are those that grow the most before winter sets in."

In addition to feeding desert critters, the saguaro provides homes for them. In this respect, the Sonoran Desert is unique among American deserts. It takes a big tree to accommodate a suitably sized nesting hole, and except along waterways, other deserts don't have enough big trees to provide a substantial number of nests. Because of its saguaros, the Sonoran Desert can. They provide many thousands of opportunities for nesting all across their sprawling range.

The two primary cavity nesters are the gilded flicker and the Gila woodpecker. In the spring they poke at the stem to make deep cavities in which to nest and hatch their eggs.

Once their young are airborne, they depart, and these cool, protected spaces become available to a dozen or more so-called secondary cavity nesters, including the tiny elf owl, songbirds, cactus wrens, and doves.

The list includes the purple martin. In the eastern United States, so many big trees were cut down that

TOP LEFT Gila woodpeckers are among the first birds to set up housekeeping in saguaros. After their eggs hatch and the young learn to fly, the woodpeckers will leave their cactus home. Tom Vezo

TOP CENTER Gilded flickers, another kind of woodpecker, also punch out cavities for a dwelling. Both kinds of woodpeckers are considered primary saguaro cactus-dwellers. Birds that move into holes vacated by woodpeckers are considered secondary dwellers. Bruce D. Taubert

TOP RIGHT This elf owl seems secure in the saguaro cavity it took over after a woodpecker departed. The cactus develops the cork-like covering to heal the wounds inflicted by birds. C.K. Lorenz

TOP Two young great horned owls are a part of the family currently occupying a nest that probably was built by another bird of prey. The youngsters may seem nervous, but they will grow to become ferocious hunters. C.K. Lorenz

CENTER Red-tailed hawk babies perch in a nest settled in a saguaro crotch. Paul and Joyce Berquist

RIGHT A great horned owl stands watch over its nest shielded by prickly saguaro arms. Tom Vezo

these birds lost their ability to use nests in trees or cliffs. They became dependent on holes provided by man, such as a complex of small spaces in the sides of buildings, or in gourds that someone has hung in a tree. But they will nest in the saguaro. For whatever reason, it is the only natural place the purple martin finds acceptable.

Harris's hawks nest in the saguaro as well, though not in cavities. These big birds perch beside their young in the safety of twig and brush nests built in the crook of the plant's strong arms.

Bobcats find shelter in the same place, but without benefit of padding. Those who've seen this phenomenon marvel at how they're able to climb up there in the first place, much less settle comfortably onto the stiletto-like cactus spines. More likely, the bobcats choose older saguaros that have lost their spines, and claw their way up on areas of the stem also devoid of spines.

A high resting place gives the bobcat respite from the pursuit of a mountain lion or hungry coyotes. Such battles play out constantly in nature, even among birds in urban settings.

Starlings, which aren't native to the Sonoran Desert and only congregate around humans, are having a real impact on the health of the urban saguaro. After the Gila woodpecker makes its home in a saguaro standing, say, on a patch of roadside ground on Tucson's east side, a European starling might come along, drive the woodpecker off and take over the nest. The woodpecker will return later and make a new nest higher up, and the process repeats.

Thus, urban saguaros are often so pockmarked with multiple cavity nests that they resemble apartment houses.

The crook formed by saguaro arms makes an ideal location for hawk nests made of twigs and brush, affording both protection and shade for the birds and their young.

TOP LEFT A young, helpless red-tailed hawk covered with white down waits for a parent to return with food. Bruce D. Taubert

TOP RIGHT Two Harris's hawks strike a pose of alertness. The older bird hunts in cooperative ventures with other adult hawks. Tom Vezo

ABOVE Something either scared this ringtail into clambering to the top of a saguaro for safety, or it scaled the cactus for a high vantage point in a search for food. A member of the raccoon family, the mammal sometimes is called a ring-tailed cat. Paul and Joyce Berquist

In winter, the cavities allow frost to invade toward the center of the stem and cause significant damage.

Whether in cities or remote areas, the plant usually has the ability to repair itself by forming a cork-like covering over the exposed flesh inside the holes, helping reduce water loss.

But too many holes can, on occasion, bring on weakness, and eventually the plant reaches its breaking point and collapses.

Death Comes to Old Granddad

Saguaros don't die the way people and animals do.

"They don't really die of old age," says the UA's Matt Johnson. "It's not like they're stricken by a heart attack or a stroke and suddenly topple over."

When a saguaro does suffer a fast death, it's often from external causes, say, a truck knocking a plant to the ground, or a half-wit blasting it to pieces with a shotgun.

Lightning is another example. In a direct hit, the saguaro will often explode. The high energy vaporizes the water inside the plant and its arms literally burst.

Normally, though, death comes at a more deliberate pace.

As the plant ages, its metabolism slows, and the resulting weakness makes it less able to cope with damage inflicted by critters and birds.

Disease can get the saguaro, too, but usually as a secondary effect of freezing. Extreme cold is the biggest enemy. It can kill the entire plant outright.

More likely, though, the freeze damage occurs only in the top 3 to 5 inches of the stem or arms, because these areas are thinner and have less mass to resist extreme temperatures.

A frost-damaged saguaro often appears as though it's rotting. In multiple spots on the plant, a brown goo breaks through the plant's external skin and oozes down the stem.

Another sign: A saguaro with its arms hanging down like a frustrated hitchhiker. The cold air kills the tissue, and the tissue can no longer support the plant's weight.

"The water in the cells freezes and that destroys the cell machinery," says the Desert Botanical Garden's McAuliffe. "Twenty degrees is the real danger point. Below that you'll see mortality."

But the absolute temperature isn't the only factor. The temperature cycle over a 24-hour period is also key.

A saguaro can survive a single cold night, but serious damage occurs if the temperature remains below freezing throughout the following day and the next night.

TOP Saguaros can take several years to die. This one, in the Lost Dutchman State Park east of Phoenix, probably won't stand much longer.
George Thomas Raymond

ABOVE The drooping arms indicate that this cactus was subjected to freezing weather. It, too, grows in the Lost Dutchman State Park.
George Thomas Raymond

This causes the surface soil and the surrounding rocks to continue to lose heat, as does the saguaro.

Early researcher Forrest Shreve studied this effect and said it explains why fewer plants survive at the northernmost boundaries of the saguaro range and at upper elevations.

The 24-hour temperature cycle isn't warm enough to support them.

And location matters. Drivers can actually see its importance at Tucson's Gates Pass, west of downtown in the Tucson Mountains.

The north-facing slopes are almost devoid of saguaros, but the rocky, south-facing slopes hold a veritable saguaro forest.

Why? South-facing slopes catch the early sun in winter, reducing the duration of cold overnight temperatures.

The periodic freezes that descend on the desert in winter are, in McAuliffe's words, minienvironmental catastrophes.

"We have them every few decades, and they really knock back the saguaro population," he says.

Old Granddad probably died from the effects of a hard freeze.

Overlooking the Rincon Valley east of Tucson, within Saguaro National Park, this saguaro had become something of a celebrity, drawing the attention of the NBC Nightly News and lots of admiring chatter among park staffers — with good reason.

It stood 40 feet tall, had between 45 and 50 arms, and was probably more than 200 years old.

No one could say with certainty how much it weighed, but guesses ranged up to 10 tons.

In October of 1992, the park's staff first noticed trouble when a volunteer reported seeing chunks of the plant's stem littering the ground beneath it. The fellow suspected vandalism. He thought someone might be pulling chunks from the stem.

A law-enforcement ranger went to have a look, and the news was worse than vandalism: The plant showed signs of bacterial necrosis, a fancy term for rotting tissue that turns black and slimy and begins oozing.

As it spreads, the freeze-damaged tissue weakens and sometimes falls off.

In other words, the plant was dying.

The park issued a news release that drew an extraordinary response.

The story of Old Granddad's demise made newspaper front pages across Arizona. Then *USA Today* picked up the story, as did media outlets as far away as Canada and Japan.

As they do in their healthy years, dead and dying saguaros fulfill a role in nature.

LEFT After more than a century, this saguaro in the east, or Rincon, unit of Saguaro National Park near Tucson is reduced to a woody skeleton with only a small amount of skin remaining. Randy Prentice

TOP With seven arms, this saguaro once was a mighty sentinel in Papago Park, located in east Phoenix. George Thomas Raymond

ABOVE Armies of insects are making use of the fallen arms of this saguaro. Paul and Joyce Berquist

Meg Weesner, the park's director of science and resources management, decided to document the plant's progression toward eventual collapse.

"I thought the best legacy Old Granddad could leave us was to tell its own story of decay," Weesner says. "We already had pictures when it was doing great. So why not have pictures of its end? After all, the time comes for everything, and Old Granddad was no different."

Park personnel set up four photo monitoring plots around the plant. They started out checking on it every week, jotting notes and taking photographs of precisely how it was changing.

At first it was losing an arm almost every week. The decay was so rapid that everyone assumed the plant's end would come quickly.

But it didn't. The staff monitoring continued month after month, though at longer and longer intervals. The rangers wrestled with the question of how to tell when a saguaro has actually died.

It's not so simple. No one issues a death certificate with a time and date in black and white.

They decided that if the plant still had green tissue, it was still photosynthesizing — turning sunlight into energy — and therefore still alive.

It took four years for Old Granddad to lose all of its green tissue.

"What was most surprising," says Weesner, "was that it had stored so many resources in those moist tissues that it was able to flower two more times, even though it was decaying."

After losing its green tissue, the plant became a standing skeleton, a collection of woody ribs that whistled in the wind.

Dead saguaros sometimes stay upright in this condition for a long time. But the remnants of Old Granddad fell to the ground within a few months.

In its long life, and also in its death, the great saguaro put on a whale of a show.

As its sister plants have done for centuries, it demonstrated remarkable resiliency and strength in its battle to maintain a place in the desert landscape.

Before its demise, the saguaro nicknamed Old Granddad drew many admirers, such as this park ranger and a visitor to the Rincon (east) unit of Saguaro National Park. At this stage, the cactus probably was more than 200 years old and had become a celebrity with the media. David Elms, Jr.

A saguaro's dying process includes many stages.

TOP LEFT Lightning felled this one.
Paul and Joyce Berquist

TOP RIGHT Poppies and lupines form a funeral bouquet
at Picacho Peak State Park south of Phoenix. Paul Gill

ABOVE LEFT A chunk of this cactus's fleshy covering
has fallen away, exposing the plant's skeleton.
Paul and Joyce Berquist

ABOVE RIGHT A young Cooper's hawk surveys the desert
from atop a saguaro skeleton. Tom Vezo

UNCERTAINTY

What We Don't Know
About Saguaros

Past Predictions
of Doom

Population Growth
Poses Real Threats

What We Don't Know About Saguaros

In spite of decades of intense curiosity and study, scientists still confront questions they cannot answer about the saguaro.

"There's an assumption that because the saguaro is so iconic, we must know everything there is to know about it," says Nature Conservancy biologist Dale Turner. "People tend to get blasé. But there's a lot we don't know."

Turner himself, along with Carianne Funicelli, studied a common problem called epidermal browning, in which the skin of a saguaro turns from green to brown, usually beginning at the base. They wanted to find out if it is a disease or an indicator of something else.

The answer is still elusive.

"It looks like it's simply an indicator," says Turner. "But we're not sure. We still don't know what drives it."

Why do saguaros not grow well in eastern Sonora, Mexico? No one can say with certainty.

Why do saguaros grow better on slopes than on flats? This phenomenon is evident off Interstate 10 between Tucson and Phoenix. Travelers between the two cities look out at the broad deserts beyond their windshields and wonder — where are all the saguaros?

One theory holds that the clay-rich soil hardens to a rocky texture when it dries, making it difficult for the saguaro to absorb water.

What causes the saguaro to branch where it does on the stem and not elsewhere?

No one knows. But in his many decades of work, Ray Turner, the retired USGS research botanist, noticed an interesting phenomenon: Saguaros seem to branch right beneath cuts in the stem, just as a rosebush will branch from the next button below a trimming.

"Saguaros produce a branch-inhibiting hormone at the tip of the stem, and it flows down," says Turner. "Well, if you injure a saguaro, one or more of the spine clusters

PRECEDING PANEL, PAGE 52 **During an August monsoon storm, lightning creates a dramatic backdrop for a stand of saguaros near Tucson.** Chuck Lawsen

LEFT **A golden haze lightly spreads over a stand of saguaros with a cholla skeleton forming a window to the dawn scene in the Cabeza Prieta National Wildlife Refuge in western Arizona.** Jack Dykinga

right below the wound will produce a branch, because you've eliminated that branch-inhibiting hormone. That's a theory I have, but it's never been tested."

Part of what gives scientists pause, and makes the saguaro such an interesting study subject, is that how a plant grows and how it lives can vary widely within a small area.

Scientists call these small areas microclimates.

A healthy saguaro stand might be accompanied, as little as a half-mile away, by an unhealthy one, depending on cover vegetation, the channeling of rainfall through the area, or the availability of rocks to serve as anchors and heat sources.

Rocky slopes make particularly good breeding grounds for new saguaros. A seed in the crevice of a boulder has found a neat hiding place for growth. It's warm, wet, and shady and protected from birds, ground squirrels, and ants that would otherwise devour it almost instantly.

In that case, the rock fills the role of the nurse plant, and the darker the rock the better.

Drive north from Phoenix on Interstate 17 and notice the saguaros growing from Black Canyon all the way up to Sunset Point. The reason is the dark rocks marking that landscape. They hold heat well and radiate it throughout 24 hours, creating a barrier against cold temperatures.

Even rocks that appear solid can provide a great home for the saguaro seed.

"I have a study plot on a giant rock that's fissured with paper-sized fractures," says Bill Peachey of the Colossal Cave park staff. "The saguaros love it because the roots go down in these little cracks and rainwater goes right down into them, too. That water doesn't evaporate or get absorbed by anything else."

The microclimate effect can even allow saguaros to live in places where, according to the textbooks at least, they don't belong.

For example, several saguaros stand on the slope of Mount Shibell, in the San Cayetano Mountains north of Nogales where the landscape is more semidesert grassland than Sonoran Desert and the 5,146-foot elevation is too high for saguaros. But there they are, surviving on that mountain when their sister saguaros down in the Santa Cruz River Valley shiver and die from winter temperatures that can tumble into single digits.

The reason? These plants stand on Mount Shibell's south-facing slope, allowing them to absorb plenty of winter sun. As cold air drains down into the valley

LEFT Along Queen Creek below Picketpost Mountain, saguaros dot a rocky slope while cottonwood trees command the terrain closest to the creek. The mixture attests to the variety of plant life that the Sonoran Desert supports in close proximity. George Stocking

TOP Saguaros thrive on a rocky, south-facing slope below Finger Rock in the Santa Catalina Mountains of the Coronado National Forest north of Tucson. Randy Prentice

ABOVE Elsewhere in the Santa Catalina Mountains, along the western face in Catalina State Park, the microclimate differs from that on the south-facing slopes. Laurence Parent

FAR LEFT Saguaros are not especially fond of snow, but if it's not too much, and the weather is not too cold, the cactuses survive. Snowy scenes such as this one in the Santa Catalina Mountains are infrequent and briefly change the desert's appearance. C.K. Lorenz

LEFT A more common winter scene in the Sonoran Desert is this one at Roosevelt Lake with snow capping the Sierra Ancha Mountains. Jerry Sieve

at night, these mountain saguaros are high enough to escape it. They are, in a sense, above the fray.

The same effect occurs above the San Pedro River northwest of Benson. Even longtime residents of that town, 40 miles east of Tucson, and nearby Pomerene, are unaware that a secret saguaro forest grows on the eastern slopes of the Little Rincon Mountains.

"There's a wintertime temperature inversion that holds cold air down the valleys," says Peachey. "It makes a little banana belt for the saguaros to grow higher up."

This variability occurs with cattle grazing as well. In many cases, it is the scourge of the saguaro.

On hot days, cattle like to gather in the shade of nurse trees, and they trample the seedlings.

But the effect isn't universal.

Ray Turner has nine study plots scattered around Arizona and Mexico. His plot at Silverbell, northwest of Tucson, as well as ones on the Tohono O'odham Indian Reservation, at Harquahala west of Phoenix, and in Sonoita, Mexico, are all grazed.

Yet they are no worse off than others that haven't been grazed.

"In a lot of desert areas without water nearby, the cattle don't make heavy use of the desert vegetation," says the botanist.

When Turner visits his study plot at McDougal Crater in Mexico's Sierra del Pinacate Reserve, he camps next to the crater, and there is a ranch nearby. He and other researchers take their nighttime entertainment from watching cattle walk along a trail to and from the ranch. They jokingly call it the cattle promenade.

The animals go to the ranch and stay there for a day to get water, then depart for a walk of several miles to a vegetation-filled arroyo and spend a couple of days eating.

When they get thirsty, they head back to the water source.

"But they just stay on the trail and go back and forth, not bothering to use the intervening country, so it doesn't get damaged," says Turner. "I'm not opposed to grazing in all instances."

So many variables about saguaros make blanket statements a dangerous endeavor. Scientists have encountered this lesson over the decades as they've trundled down blind alleys and fallen off research cliffs.

Some have even convinced themselves that the life-clock of the saguaro species is ticking down to silence.

But is it really?

Past Predictions of Doom

Predictions of doom have been around a long time.

In 1988, *Newsweek* stated that Arizona's saguaros were vanishing, and three years later, *The New York Times* echoed the warning.

Surely, more scientifically astute publications have avoided the hand-wringers' chorus? Not quite.

"A wonderful plant doomed," declared *Plant World* magazine.

The date of that story? 1902.

So … are saguaros going extinct?

It would take some disaster to bring that about, for the saguaro population runs into the millions.

Consider that Saguaro National Park comprises about 91,000 acres with a saguaro population estimated at 1.6 million. Other protected areas with comparable saguaro densities include: Organ Pipe Cactus National Monument, abutting the Mexican border, consisting of 330,000 acres; immediately to its west, the Cabeza Prieta National Wildlife Refuge, which has 860,000 acres. But even these desert parcels pale in size compared to the Barry M. Goldwater Air Force Range, west of the Cabeza — it measures a whopping 1.6 million acres. The military uses some of that land for test bombing, but the majority is left alone.

No, the saguaro isn't going extinct. These vast tracts of protected land practically guarantee that won't happen.

But the talk of disaster is in some ways understandable. The saguaro, you see, is a bit of a trickster: It reproduces episodically, with periods of population growth interrupted by periods of decline.

This characteristic, along with its great ability to rebound when climatic conditions turn in its favor, makes predictions iffy.

"Saguaro populations decline and grow, decline and grow, and the cycles are longer than our lifetime," says Joe McAuliffe, the research director at Phoenix's Desert Botanical Garden. "They can take place over centuries, and many fluctuations are still going on. So we might see declines and think the saguaro is disappearing. Not necessarily."

LEFT Refusing to fall over, this saguaro skeleton forms an arch highlighting the three cactuses living near it in the Tonto National Forest near Mesa. George Thomas Raymond

ABOVE Backlight dramatizes a stand of cactuses in Picacho Peak State Park. A variety of cactus species, desert shrubs, and goldpoppies inhabit the area. George Stocking

As an example, McAuliffe cites the alarm bells sounded in 1940 when researchers claimed that the great saguaro forest at Tucson's Saguaro National Monument — redesignated a park in 1994 — was dying.

It was huge news.

After all, the desire to protect this stunning landscape prompted the founding of the monument in the first place in 1933 with the signing of a proclamation by Herbert Hoover in the last days of his presidency.

The supposed cause of the saguaro die-off was bacterial necrosis, which many scientists then believed was a disease. This theory held sway into the 1970s and later.

But it was dead wrong. The culprit was nothing more exotic than cold weather, specifically a hard freeze in 1937, during which temperatures in Tucson fell to 15°.

The cold so damaged the giant saguaros that their tissues began a process of bacterial decomposition. The process was entirely natural. There was no disease.

But mature saguaros at the monument were indeed dying off at an alarming rate. So what was the real cause?

As is usually the case in saguaro research, scientists found the answer only after taking a long-term view.

The problem began in the late 1800s when settlers, drawn by two perennial streams, made homes in what would become monument land and brought cattle with them.

The animals trampled the seedlings. Cattle were allowed to graze in the cactus forest until 1958.

In addition, settlers chopped down mesquite and paloverde trees to use the wood as fuel in their lime kilns. This eliminated nurse plants that otherwise would have sheltered the next generation of baby saguaros.

As McAuliffe has noted in his writing, these practices virtually eliminated saguaro establishment in some parts of the monument from 1900 through about 1960.

Researchers pay attention to both living and dead saguaros and to climate conditions in trying to determine why saguaro cactuses have experienced periods of decline. Tom Vezo

This phenomenon, coupled with the death of older plants, produced the decline at that portion of the monument that had everyone in a tizzy.

In the *Sonoran Quarterly* in 1993, McAuliffe wrote: "What had been an extraordinary cactus forest when the monument was created in the early 1930s became a landscape from which tall, branched saguaros were all but absent by the early 1980s."

Since then, however, these saguaros have mounted a wonderful comeback, confounding those who predicted their disappearance by the year 2000.

Ray Turner, who has been monitoring study plots in the great saguaro forest since 1959, expressed surprise at the scope of the comeback.

"It took many years under the right conditions for a lot of seeds to germinate, and boy, they've done it in leaps and bounds," he says. "We have another plot at Saguaro [Park] West, in the Tucson Mountains, and this is another place where they've skyrocketed

and I have no idea why. I'll tell you, the saguaro is outsmarting me."

Also in 1993, the National Park Service asked McAuliffe, an ecologist, to review 50 years worth of studies at the park to help understand what had led scientists astray. He concluded that those who predicted extinction from bacterial necrosis "completely misinterpreted what was going on."

Says McAuliffe: "The main players were not ecologists with a wide range of training. They were plant pathologists and that was the world they saw, a world ruled by microbes. They failed to look at things more holistically."

Remarkably, similar mistakes of interpretation began reappearing in the 1990s.

This time, the doomsday talk about saguaros at the park centered on air pollution, toxic residue from mining activity, and epidermal browning caused by increased ultraviolet radiation from a diminishing ozone layer.

This rocky terrain shows saguaros of various ages — older ones with arms; younger ones that have yet to grow arms; and the youngest ones, tucked away in the bosoms of nurse plants. Tom Vezo

McAuliffe scrutinized these studies as well, and concluded that they're bunk, driven less by fact than by politics and sloppy science.

What is it about the saguaro that seems to attract so much shaky research?

McAuliffe has an interesting theory on that.

The plant's status as a celebrity, an icon of the desert, draws research money, and that in turn attracts scientists with the time to study it from the perspective of their particular disciplines. But it takes wise effort to get from early fascination to really learning about the plant and its interactions with other life forms, with man, and with the climate.

"Many factors affect saguaro biology," says McAuliffe. "Some affect the ability of young ones to establish, and others affect the mortality of old plants. But twice now we've had people trained in narrow specialties who were unable to see the big picture, and they misinterpreted the data."

Saguaros have a way of blurring the big picture, however. The microclimate effect, for example, makes it hard to draw broad conclusions from small study plots.

But Ray Turner and research partner Betsy Pierson have provided what might be the best big-picture look at saguaro health ever taken. It is based on those nine study plots that Turner established in 1959 with then-partner James Rodney Hastings.

The plots are all in the central and northern parts of the saguaro range — such as in the Harquahala Mountains west of Phoenix, at Redington on the San Pedro River, on the Tohono O'odham Indian Reservation west of Tucson, and at McDougal Crater in Mexico's Sierra del Pinacate Reserve.

Turner has returned to each plot every eight to 10 years to measure progress, and recently, with Pierson, analyzed all the complicated data collected from a half-century of work.

Their conclusion? About half the study plots showed a slight decline in saguaros over time, but others have shown remarkable increases.

"My feeling is that the drought over the past decade might be causing a very slow decline," says Turner. "But it's not threatening the total population by any means."

Something else might be, though.

It's not cactus rustlers, the nasty crooks who dig up saguaros and sell them on a thriving black market.

Saguaros turn into silhouettes at sunset, while the sky and clouds grow darker in the Avra Valley west of Tucson.
Randy Prentice

It's not the illegal migrants who pour across Arizona's border with Mexico, trampling precious desert environments.

This threat is much simpler, entirely legal, and visible everywhere.

Just visit any Arizona city and look around at all the people living there, and all the new ones coming in.

The threat is us. The threat is growth.

Population Growth Poses Real Threats

The numbers tell the story resoundingly. Arizona's population in 1970 was 1.7 million; in 2010, it's projected to be 6.6 million. More people mean more subdivisions, highways, shopping centers, and pavement — a good portion of which eliminates land on which saguaros grow.

To save saguaros from the bulldozer, some towns and counties have passed ordinances requiring, in some circumstances, that they be transplanted instead.

But results have been mixed, according to Lisa Harris, of the Harris Environmental Group, a Tucson consulting firm specializing in natural and cultural resources.

In a 10-year study of transplanted saguaros, Harris and six other researchers found that a 3-foot plant with no arms has a good chance of survival after removal to a new location.

But for saguaros more than 6 feet tall, the survival rate goes way down. And the bigger, multiarmed saguaros are the most coveted, and therefore the most transplanted.

When workers move a saguaro, they usually dig right under its base, then plop the plant down again in its new home. This causes it to lose the support network of fine roots that fan out around it.

"Because of all the saguaro's built-in mass, it sometimes takes years for them to die," says Harris. "When a transplanted saguaro dies, it's usually not attributed to the transplant. But that's what caused it."

Those who wrote the laws, and the transplanters, had good intentions. But they didn't understand the biology of the saguaro.

"They spend a lot of money, think they're doing good, but the big plants usually don't survive," says Harris.

She offers an alternative: Ask if it's really necessary to pull out that majestic saguaro. And if it is, can it be replaced with three or four smaller ones more likely to survive?

Right below growth on the threat chart — and for some scientists, above it — is the problem of wildfires fueled by exotic grasses.

In most areas of the saguaro range, the landscape has never had enough fuel to carry a continuous fire, one that spreads out across an entire valley, or up the side of a mountain.

Now it does, and the main culprits are red brome, fountain grass, and especially buffelgrass.

Most agree that the latter, an African perennial grass first brought to North America to provide more forage for cattle, has the most destructive potential.

After native plants have been burned off, buffelgrass grows back even faster, and that means future fires will be more frequent and hotter, according to a study by the National Park Service.

To bring seed regrowth back to prefire conditions, the saguaro might need 20 years, according to the bulletin *Park Science*, which reported the study's results, and even longer to replace mature saguaro stands.

But fast-growing buffelgrass won't wait, and it might, in effect, take over the desert, eventually replacing native plants.

Buffelgrass first appeared along roadsides at Saguaro National Park, in the east end of the Tucson Valley, in 1993.

It has since spread into dry washes and over remote slopes.

"I'm very concerned," says Meg Weesner, the park's director of science. "Four years ago we did an inventory and we had 400 acres infested with buffelgrass. Now that's probably up to 1,000 acres. But 10,000 acres are susceptible to it, and that would be a really big chunk of where saguaros grow here."

The same spread is occurring at Organ Pipe Cactus National Monument, and at 129,000-acre Ironwood Forest National Monument, northwest of Tucson — two areas where the saguaro is protected from its other main threat, development.

The long-term impact?

"I think buffelgrass is going to remake the desert ecosystem," says Dale Turner of The Nature Conservancy.

He notes that plant communities are "dynamic assemblages," constantly changing, and the collection of plants that now defines the Sonoran Desert, including the saguaro, is a relatively new phenomenon. In other words, the desert has always been a work in progress, a continuous cycle in which some plant species take hold and others disappear.

Turner fears the remade desert of the future might not include saguaros.

"With invasive grasses and climate change, we now have a much greater incidence of fire in the Sonoran Desert, and that has the potential for eliminating saguaros from a substantial percentage of their range.

LEFT Arizona's population growth, exemplified by this image taken from the base of Phoenix's Piestewa Peak, poses threats to the saguaro cactus.
Randy Prentice

TOP AND ABOVE The colors of sunset and a fire are virtually the same. An extensive fire raged through a portion of the east unit of Saguaro National Park near Tucson in 1994 and damaged or killed many saguaros.
Paul and Joyce Berquist

"Now it's entirely possible that we'll import some plant species, or some organism will evolve that will control buffelgrass. But that hasn't happened yet."

This view might sound extreme, but an increasing number of scientists see the same danger, and some go further.

They point to the explosion of buffelgrass in Sonora, Mexico, where the government and ranchers actually plant it.

It's a hardy grass that stays green in May and June, allowing ranchers to keep their cattle on the land at a time when they normally couldn't, for lack of food.

In some cases, cattlemen clear-cut desert vegetation from large swaths of landscape, until nothing remains to offer competition for this foreign plant.

Soon, because it grows so quickly, the landscape consists of buffelgrass and little else.

From Sonora, buffelgrass seed migrates north just as people do. It comes in on clothing and on shoes, stuck on the tires of smugglers' trucks, and even on the wind.

Unlike other questions about the saguaro, which take many decades or longer to answer, the potential threat from fire and buffelgrass will play out relatively quickly.

In fact, this threat is unfolding many times faster than the rate of urban development.

"Certainly within two decades," says Matt Johnson, the UA's Desert Legume Program manager, "we'll have a very clear idea of whether or not we're losing this battle."

LEFT Like a sentinel, a saguaro casts its shadow over Mexican goldpoppies in Picacho Peak State Park between Phoenix and Tucson. G.C. Kelley

ABOVE There's water out there, and the line of saguaro cactuses defines a desert drainage, variously called a wash or an arroyo. The scene lies near the Antelope Hills in the Cabeza Prieta National Wildlife Refuge in western Arizona. Jack Dykinga

SEARCHING

Hunting for the
Tallest Saguaro

Commonly Asked
Questions

Hunting for the Tallest Saguaro

Another battle, this one delightfully less sobering, rages across Arizona's cactus country every two years. It involves the hunt for the tallest saguaro. As the biggest of a big breed, this plant automatically achieves exalted status, that of a champion, the equivalent of baseball's home run king. Desert lovers talk about it, fret over it, and gaze upon it with worshipful eyes.

Old Granddad was such a saguaro.

"Boy, what a tree that was," says former nursery owner Ken Morrow, who spends his retirement years hunting big trees. "Big trunk, reasonably tall, lots of arms, a really dominant plant. We've been trying to live up to it ever since."

Morrow works with a conservation group, American Forests, which every two years publishes its *National Register of Big Trees*. The book names record-holders across the United States, including saguaros in Arizona.

But the *Register* doesn't name winners based solely on height. Instead, it employs a formula that awards a point total based on circumference, plus height, plus average crown spread.

Using those criteria, Arizona has co-champion saguaros — one in the Tonto National Forest, near Horseshoe Lake, the other above the San Pedro River about 5 miles east of San Manuel, in southern Arizona.

These plants rack up totals of 143 and 144 points respectively. The *Register* names co-champions if two trees come within five points of each other.

But these are two very different specimens.

The Horseshoe Lake plant, known as the Grand One, stands 46 feet tall. The San Manuel plant measures a "mediocre" 32 feet tall, but it makes the top of the list because of its eye-popping 108-inch circumference.

"Our motto is girth first," says Morrow, the *Register's* Arizona state coordinator. "That's where you get the bulk of your points."

For a couple of reasons, champions usually don't stay champions for long.

PRECEDING PANEL, PAGE 70 This mighty saguaro in the Sonoran Desert National Monument's Sand Tank Mountains, located in the desert country southwest of Phoenix, probably ranks in the upper reaches of saguaro size. Those who measure saguaros award points for a cactus's height, circumference, and average crown spread. Jack Dykinga

LEFT This scene at sunset near Carefree, north of Phoenix, depicts an iconic Arizona image so dramatic that it sometimes is used to represent other areas of the West, where saguaros don't even grow. Jerry Jacka

LEFT Look closely to the right and just below the saguaro in the foreground. That's a mule deer buck standing in a wash in the west unit of Saguaro National Park. Tom Danielsen

RIGHT A family hikes in the midst of a stand of saguaros for a close-up look. George H.H. Huey

For one, the saguaro is so popular that competitors are constantly being located to knock record-holders from their pedestals.

Also, the fall-down factor adds to the high turnover of champions. In addition to being tall, these saguaros are invariably old and heavy, often with multiple arms, making them vulnerable to strong winds.

Two examples:

- A co-champion on the north shore of Arizona's Roosevelt Lake collapsed during the wet winter of 2000. It was 43 feet tall.
- A record-holder from the 1996 *Register*, off Vulture Mine Road outside Wickenburg, lost its spot the following year, probably from a lightning strike.

Interestingly, the Vulture Mine saguaro, initially listed as 54 feet tall, actually was 4 feet shorter.

In the business of saguaro hunting, inaccurate measurements are common.

In his pursuit of the biggest of the big, Morrow relies on half a dozen informants who spend their free time scouting the backcountry. They generally provide solid measurements.

But he also sifts through tips from amateurs whose field work can be, well, questionable at best.

To prove a case, an amateur often includes a photograph showing Aunt Hilda standing at the foot of the supposed new champ.

If she's 5 feet tall, then the saguaro behind her must be … 56 feet tall!

When Morrow does his own measurement, the 56 feet usually turns out to be 46.

"They want it to be 56 feet tall, so it is," says Morrow. "Hope is a big part of this."

Pride, too. Lots of folks want to puff out their chests to claim they've found the biggest saguaro.

Take the retired Mesa man whose fondest wish was to have the saguaro in his front yard entered in the record book. To make it come true, he watered his plant relentlessly, turning it into a real fatty. In the unlikely event that passersby missed the obese specimen, this fellow erected a not-so-subtle sign declaring: World's Largest Saguaro!

In spite of its girth, the plant wasn't tall enough to make the *Register*, and the man's heart broke when he heard the painful truth.

Like amateurs, old pros harbor dreams, too, and Morrow's is to one day find the mythical 150-point saguaro.

"I know it's out there," he says.

Until he finds it, he remains steadfast in his determination to resist rumors that somewhere, in some remote corner of the desert, a 60- to 70-foot-tall saguaro awaits his high-tech measuring gear.

"Fifty feet is amazing to get, so I'm not going to be pulled in by talk of a 60- to 70-footer," says Morrow. "Until I see it myself, I'm not buying it."

As for naming the tallest saguaro ever measured, that's a complicated matter.

The greatest height for a scientifically measured standing saguaro, according to writer Carle Hodge, was slightly less than 53 feet. It had only three arms.

The plant stood in the Tucson Mountains and fell over in the summer of 1975.

The 1996 *Guinness Book of World Records* listed a 57-foot, 11³/₄-inch-tall saguaro in the Maricopa Mountains east of Gila Bend as the "tallest cactus."

But as Hodge pointed out in his book *All About Saguaros*, the plant was actually taller than that — 59 feet tall.

Morrow was on his way to formally measure this giant when it toppled over. But he saw pictures of it in the September 1991 issue of *Arizona Highways* and was mightily impressed.

"It looked to be 54 or 55 feet tall," he says. "But you never know until you do the actual measurement."

In 2004, volunteer investigator Mike Hallen found the tallest saguaro ever recorded by the *Register*. This plant, located just east of Florence, stands 51 feet tall. Because it is midsized in circumference, it garnered only 140 points.

But that puts it within five points of the Horseshoe Lake and San Manuel saguaros, earning the 51-footer a listing as one of three champions in the 2008 *Register*.

Hallen named the plant Flo, after the nearby town — his mom is also named Florence — and now, when he's out indulging his weekend saguaro-hunting hobby, he sometimes stops to check on his biggest find.

"I look at the old ones like grandparents sitting in a rocking chair at the nursing home," says Hallen, a Phoenix postal worker. "You want to visit to see how they're doing."

And how is Flo getting on?

"Oh, she's doing just fine," says Hallen. "I think that cactus is going to be around a long time."

Commonly Asked Questions

In addition to asking about the tallest saguaro, tour guides and others in the saguaro business say that ordinary folks commonly ask five other questions:

- How many arms does a saguaro grow?
- How many saguaros are there throughout the Sonoran Desert?
- What causes a crested saguaro, those funny-shaped plants that fan out at the top?
- If the saguaro is first, what comes in second as the world's tallest cactus?
- How can you tell how old a saguaro is?

On the age question, scientists have always had little to go on, relying mainly on year-to-year measurements of growth rates, which scientists use to make age approximations.

But researchers have always longed for a more exact way to date saguaros. The wait might be over.

Nathan English, a Ph.D. in geosciences from the University of Arizona, has come up with an innovative method similar to tree-ring dating. When a saguaro grows, it uses atmospheric carbon dioxide to build its tissues. English analyzes the saguaro's spines to determine the ratio of radioactive carbon to stable carbon, and from this he can determine when a particular spine grew.

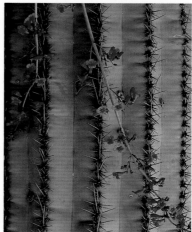

FAR LEFT Sometimes, casual observers report finding a cactus that seems to be 60 or more feet tall. Not hardly, as a John Wayne character said in response to reports of his death. The height of this cactus, pointing to the moon hovering over the west unit of Saguaro National Park, is accentuated by the camera's upward perspective. Joe Zinn

TOP Two famous Phoenix-area scenes — a rocky slope punctuated with saguaros and the Four Peaks of the Sierra Ancha Mountains — combine to illustrate the diversity of the Sonoran Desert. Paul Gill

ABOVE A saguaro shares its space with a penstemon, a member of the snapdragon family. Jack Dykinga

"If it grew between 1955 and today, I can date it to within a couple of years," says English.

Why 1955? That year the Soviet Union and the United States began frequent atmospheric nuclear testing, which put radioactive carbon into the atmosphere.

The chemistry of spines also provides clues to climatic conditions at various stages of its growth.

Using his radiocarbon method, in conjunction with growth curves established by other researchers, English can even estimate, to within a decade, the age of saguaros that germinated in the 1870s.

Farther back than that, estimates grow much more uncertain. But English's work has given scientists a dating tool they've never had before.

Regarding the other common questions:

How many arms can a saguaro grow?

No one has studied the matter to determine a normal number of arms, or a maximum number. But some plants can be extremely productive.

Remember, producing arms is what the survival instinct has taught the saguaro to do. More growth stems mean more fruit, flowers, and seeds, and this gives the plant a better shot at reproduction.

Generally, though, a saguaro has a chance to grow multiple arms if it stands in well-drained soil with sufficient rock content to anchor the plant against strong winds.

It's no accident that the biggest saguaros are on mountain slopes, or at the top of the bajada, the debris area that water runoff forms at the base of mountains.

Conversely, it's unusual to find giant, multiarmed saguaros standing on flat valley floors.

Sooner or later, a combination of wet soil and strong winds will knock the plant down.

Moisture holds the key, both in how often a saguaro branches and how high on the stem the branch appears, according to Joe McAuliffe.

For example, saguaros around Tucson, where annual rainfall reaches 10 inches, grow their first arms lower on the main stem than saguaros in Arizona's drier western deserts.

TOP Cold weather at a critical stage of a saguaro's development can cause it to sprout twisted arms.
George Stocking

LEFT How many arms can a saguaro grow? Researchers have not studied the matter. With arms on its arms, this one, near the lower Salt River in the Tonto National Forest, is said to be bearing 100 arms. Paul Gill

How many saguaros are there?

Counting them is a Herculean task. Is it even possible to look at every piece of ground within the saguaro range, from every direction, and make a reasonable count, including baby saguaros hidden under nurse plants?

No, it isn't. But two Tucson-based researchers think they've found a way to make a reasonable guess.

Bill Thornton and Gary Christopherson, director of the University of Arizona's Center for Applied Spatial Analysis, are using Ray Turner's four-decade-old test plots to arrive at an average saguaro density.

They'll multiply that number by the size of the plant's range, with subtractions for the estimated amount of land within the range that doesn't have saguaros, to produce an estimate.

"Because cactus populations are cyclical, we know we're shooting at a moving target," says Thornton, a retiree who contributes articles to the *Cactus and Succulent Journal*. "Whatever number we come up with will be very rough."

The study isn't completed yet. But Thornton believes the number won't be less than 25 million and could be as high as 75 million.

In the Tucson region alone, experts estimate there are more than 3 million saguaros, a number that outstrips the human population by three to one.

If the saguaro is the tallest cactus, what comes in second?

Hold on. The saguaro isn't the world's tallest cactus. But Joe McAuliffe says it's sometimes hard to convince people of that point.

Representatives of the Canadian Broadcasting Corporation contacted him to request help on a show they were producing on how saguaros deal with extreme heat.

When he read the script, McAuliffe encountered the same old problem — fascination not backed by facts. He found that the writer had named the saguaro the biggest cactus in the world.

"The saguaro is so iconic that people think it is the only plant like it in the whole world, and the biggest," says McAuliffe. "It isn't."

In fact, the saguaro — known by the scientific name, *Carnegiea gigantea* — isn't even the tallest cactus in the Sonoran Desert. The "tallest" honor goes to the cardón cactus, *Pachycereus pringlei*.

The saguaro population may number between 25 million and 75 million. Along with the spines of other thorny plants, such as the cholla and ocotillo in this scene at Gates Pass in Tucson Mountain Park, that's a lot of points that can stick you. Tom Vezo

This monster, a different species entirely, grows up to 65 feet tall, and its stem can reach nearly 5 feet in diameter. It can weigh 30 tons.

The untrained eye often confuses it with the saguaro. The cardón, however, branches much closer to the ground, and its branches don't go as far sideways before heading up. Their reach is almost straight to the sky.

The cardón grows widely across the Baja California Peninsula and south along Mexico's west coast. Its far northern limit is west of Caborca, Sonora, just south of the United States border.

Another cactus species, found in central Mexico, can even reach 80 feet in height.

What causes a saguaro to crest?
Cresting is basically a mutation, and it happens in many plants. Scientists call it fasciation. Instead of the cells on the growing tip dividing in symmetrical fashion and making a rounded stem, they divide laterally, causing the plant to grow sideways at the top.

In the saguaro, this mutation creates a visually captivating, fan-like effect that can range up to 9 feet wide.

Its cause remains unknown, although theories abound, from frost and infection, to the most far-fetched possibility, lightning strikes.

At one time, researchers thought only 200 crests existed, but recent counts have pushed the number to 640.

Because of its rarity, and its bizarre shape, the crested saguaro, also called a cristate, is a kind of botanical cult figure. It attracts dedicated followers who record sightings of the plant in the same way others report seeing Bigfoot.

LEFT Researchers are not sure why crests have formed atop an estimated 640 saguaros. This one is in the North Maricopa Mountains Wilderness. Jerry Sieve

ABOVE Despite its beauty, a crest on a saguaro is a mutation that causes the plant to grow sideways at the top. C.K. Lorenz

LORE

The Saguaro in
Western Legend

As Used by the
Tohono O'odham

The Tohono O'odham
Saguaro Creation
Story

The Saguaro in Western Legend

Throughout history, the saguaro has found itself at the center of exaggeration and legend.

Think of a man living on Arizona's frontier.

He's wearing a big hat, boots that go jingle-jangle, and a fringed jacket that's too clean and well-kept to be anything but decoration.

He's sitting behind a glass of really horrible whiskey in a shack-like saloon telling a story that shouldn't, by any reasonable standard, attract a single believer.

But because it's about the great saguaro, this mystery in the desert, it attracts a bunch of them, and their eyes are round with attention.

Joe Mulhatton was such a man.

He lived in Florence, southeast of Phoenix, an area where saguaros grow as thick as the tales, and we remember him because the tale he told, in 1899, was picked up by several newspapers around the Territory.

Our man Joe claimed that giant saguaros around Florence exerted an extraordinary magnetic force, probably, he theorized, from vast beds of copper running beneath the earth. Because of this great power, each plant could attract or repel any object that drew close.

In his story, Mulhatton told of two unsuspecting tramps who took refuge underneath some of these monsters and of the grisly disaster that ensued. He wrote:

"One of the men was at once drawn up to and impaled on the sharp blades of the cactus, while the octopus-like arms folded around him crushing him through and into the cactus, where his blood, flesh and bones turned into a pulp very much like ordinary mucilage, which trickled out slowly from the aperture made by the passing in of the man's body.

"The cactus loses its magnetic power while it is digesting its victim. So we were enabled to look at this wonderful yet gruesome sight and report these particulars."

A negative cactus repelled the second tramp and heaved his body about 100 feet against a positive one, whereupon he met the same fate.

PRECEDING PANEL, PAGE 82 The saguaro plays a prominent role in Southwestern lore. This stand lies in southwestern Arizona's Cabeza Prieta National Wildlife Refuge along El Camino del Diablo, the infamous Devil's Road on which Indians, Spanish explorers, and gold-seeking forty-niners traveled to California through near-waterless desert. If travelers from centuries ago could return there, they would see in essence the same scene through which they had traveled. Cabeza Prieta draws its name from the "dark head" of a lava-topped mountain range in the refuge. George Stocking

LEFT This mighty saguaro near Florence is as twisted as the tale that such a cactus exerted a force strong enough to overpower a man and draw him to its spines and devour him, as a magnet attracts a nail. Paul Gill

TOP In the Tohono O'odham Indian account of the saguaro's creation, a flower-bearing cactus emerged from the spot where a young girl had sunk into the earth and disappeared. Jack Dykinga

ABOVE Drooping and gangling arms cast a comedic appearance onto this saguaro. Dave Bly

Mulhatton's story originally ran in the *Florence Tribune*, and it so impressed the editors of the *Tombstone Epitaph* that they printed a subsequent version with added details.

It seems Mulhatton himself approached to within 100 feet of one of these man-eating cactuses, but it was "all he could do to resist its influence to draw him in."

He then returned to town to fetch a rope, planning to tie it around his waist while four of his friends wrapped their arms around him and held on.

Mulhatton wanted to "approach near enough to minutely examine the wonder without danger."

A traveling salesman in his work life, brave Joe, we can assume, was accustomed to approaching thorny customers. In telling his story, however, there is something more going on than a prankster creating nonsense for kerosene-lamp entertainment.

At the bottom of the *Tribune* version, Mulhatton concluded: "There is very little travel through this wild section of Arizona, or this species of cactus would have been written about sooner."

Note the implicit danger in that statement, the romance and the mystery. What's out there? Will I survive it? Am I tough enough?

Everyone who ever braved the Western frontier has asked those questions.

The man-eating cactus was less a story than an invitation — a dare to test ourselves against "wild Arizona," using the saguaro as the lure.

Isn't that what cities, businesses, and chambers of commerce still do today?

Joe Mulhatton was an early practitioner of the art of promotion, a pioneer in more ways than one.

In the Tohono O'odham saguaro creation story, a bird, such as one that might live in the hole in this plant, helped a girl find a village. For this kindness, the saguaro allowed birds to be the first to eat its fruit each year. Tom Vezo

As Used by the Tohono O'odham

For Indians living within the saguaro range, the saguaro has always provided something far more practical — food.

Even in times of severe drought, the saguaro blooms and produces fruit, which, in turn, can be made into syrup, sweet jam, butter, flour, chicken feed, pinole, hot drinks, snacks, summer drinks, and more.

A number of tribes — Pima, Maricopa, Yaqui, Apache — have relied on the saguaro to stay alive in hard times.

But for the Tohono O'odham, who live in desert villages north and west of Tucson, the plant is as much a part of life as blue sky.

These Indians consider it a sacred tree and afford it a central place in their cultural and spiritual lives.

The O'odham base their annual calendar around the saguaro, beginning each year with the fruit harvest of late June or early July.

Immediately thereafter, right before the first rains, they hold their most important annual ceremony, the *navaita*.

In this ancient ritual, tribal members try to "bring down the clouds" by singing, dancing, and drinking wine made from the fermented syrup of the saguaro fruit.

By saturating their bodies with this slightly nauseating, crimson-colored wine, the O'odham believe they're mimicking the saturation of the earth with rain — and actually bringing it about.

But the saguaro gives them more than wine for rain-making and food for their empty stomachs. It provides the raw materials by which the people can build their lives.

Even the uses listed here are testimony not only to the cleverness of the people but also to this plant's seemingly unending bounty.

From the woody ribs, the O'odham build brush huts, cradles, and children's carrying baskets.

TOP The saguaro cactus fruit provides a yearly treat to the Tohono O'odham, or "people of the desert."
Paul and Joyce Berquist

MIDDLE Birds and native desert dwellers savor the seedy fruit of the saguaro. David Elms, Jr.

RIGHT This person is harvesting saguaro fruit with a pole fashioned from saguaro ribs. The fruit harvest on the Tohono O'odham Reservation begins in late June or early July, a time that is at the heart of the O'odham calendar. David Elms, Jr.

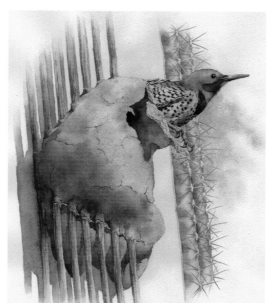

The ribs can also be fashioned into dice for playing games and lances for hunting. They can be split to make rough traps for catching quail or laid out to make racks for drying fruit.

Hunters pull their deer sinew bowstrings through a small hole in saguaro wood to smooth them out.

Saguaro spines burn so brightly and so fast that they make perfect kindling for nighttime signal fires.

Four of these spines tied in a row make a piercing instrument for applying tattoos.

Even after the plant dies and falls over, it keeps producing.

Calloused-over bird holes emerge from the debris, and these so-called saguaro "boots" become handy carrying bins for a variety of personal items.

The saguaro is a plant for all seasons and purposes, and it never disappoints because to the Tohono O'odham it is one of them.

The Tohono O'odham Saguaro Creation Story

For more than 150 years, writers, botanists, and ethnographers have traveled O'odham land, listened to tribal stories about the origin of the saguaro, and repeated those oral accounts in their articles.

The vast majority are written by non-Indians, and most involve an O'odham child sinking into the earth and re-emerging as a giant saguaro.

These stories are valuable as snapshots of early tribal life. But the non-Indian chronicler invariably encounters barriers of language, culture, and belief.

Wouldn't it be better to have the same story written by a Tohono O'odham?

Rare as it is, Susie Ignacio Enos offered just such an account in *Arizona Quarterly* in 1945.

She told the beautiful story of an Aw'awtam (O'odham) girl named Sugu-ik Oof.

When she was 10, Sugu-ik Oof's mother left to go to the village to get food. The girl followed after her, but didn't know the way.

LEFT When these fixtures of the Sonoran Desert — saguaros and a late-afternoon summer monsoon — get together, they project a powerful, yet startlingly beautiful scene, such as this one in the west unit of Saguaro National Park. Jack Dykinga

TOP AND ABOVE The illustrations show how a callus, commonly called a "boot," is pierced by a saguaro's inner ribs and protrudes beyond the skin to form a gourd-like structure. The callus process begins when a woodpecker (top) or a flicker pecks a hole through the saguaro's outer skin to form a hole for nesting. The irritation causes chemicals to flow in the saguaro to heal the wound. Eventually a very hard boot is formed. Kevin Kibsey

As she walked, Sugu-ik Oof met a coyote and later a rabbit, and each offered to help her find the village. But in return they wanted one of the gourds she carried.

Then Sugu-ik Oof met a little gray bird, who offered to guide her for nothing, but the bird couldn't go all the way into the village because the little boys there always shot arrows and threw rocks at birds.

Sugu-ik Oof told the bird that one day her kindness would be repaid.

With the bird's help, she reached the village and asked the children where her mother was, but they refused to answer.

Sugu-ik Oof began to chant a song, and still the children ignored her. By the time they looked at her, she had sunk halfway into the ground.

The children screamed and ran to get Sugu-ik Oof's mother.

But she came too late. The little girl already had disappeared into the ground, and no amount of tears could bring her back.

The mother returned repeatedly to the place where her daughter had sunk into the earth and put down food and water.

After a year, an odd-looking plant rose there, and Sugu-ik Oof's mother cared for it as it grew.

But time passed, and she became old and feeble.

One day after the coldest time of the year, a beautiful white flower appeared on the plant, and the whole village was excited.

After the flower had gone, a fruit formed and burst into scarlet red.

Sugu-ik Oof's mother watched the birds eat the fruit, and, after it fell to the ground, she ate some. It was delicious, and the people liked it, too.

TOP Prehistoric people pecked their art depicting animals, the sun, and other forms into rocks. The petroglyphs are spread over an area called Signal Hill, in the west unit of Saguaro National Park. Jeff Snyder

LEFT People of the Salado culture in the 13th, 14th, and early 15th centuries lived in this cliff dwelling, preserved at Tonto National Monument near Roosevelt Lake. Their disparate homeland consisted of a river valley, steep slopes, hillsides, and mesas. Plants on which they depended included saguaros on the hillsides and mesas and mesquite, walnut, and sycamore trees in the flood plains. Deer, rabbits, quail, and other game flourished in this setting. George H.H. Huey

Every year after that the *hash'an,* as the people called the saguaro, bore the same flower and fruit, and everyone came to eat it.

But the people got angry because the birds could reach the fruit easier than they could.

So the children began to shoot the birds with arrows and throw rocks to chase them away.

One day at ripening the children ran out to get the fruit before the birds, but the plant had disappeared.

The people were sad because they loved the delicious fruit and feared evil spirits were at work.

Following a great council, the people decided to hunt for the plant. After much searching, the little gray bird found it on a mountainside.

When everyone from the village went to ask the plant why it had tried to disappear, the plant told of the little gray bird helping to find the village and of its promise to reward that kindness.

The plant said: "Now that I am a *hash'an*, I can help the birds. They will be the first to eat of my fruit when it is ripe. When I stood near the village, the Aw'awtam children used to shoot and throw rocks at the birds when they tried to eat of my fruit, but I didn't like that. If the birds couldn't eat of my fruit, then no one else could."

TOP LEFT A variety of birds and other creatures soon will converge on the fruit-bearing cactuses in the west unit of Saguaro National Park. Randy Prentice

TOP RIGHT These young gilded flickers are waiting for their parents to come home with food. Thin-billed flickers punch holes near the top of a saguaro because the trunk is less dense there. Bruce D. Taubert

ABOVE A white-winged dove feasts on saguaro fruit. Bruce D. Taubert

Then and there, man, beast, and fowl declared that all should eat the fruit of the *hash'an*.

With that decision, a prophecy told to Sugu-ik Oof's father had come true.

On his deathbed, the man had summoned his 1-year-old daughter to tell her that the tribe's wise man had appeared to him.

The wise man had a message for Sugu-ik Oof — and it was that she would be different from woman.

She would grow to be great, known by races of people far and wide, and she would save generations of Aw'awtam from starvation.

She would, the wise man promised, live to the end of times as queen of the desert lands.

The shapes and growth patterns of saguaros seem as endless as the sky blazoned by sunset in the Cabeza Prieta National Wildlife Refuge, a few miles west of Papago Well. Robert McDonald

Banks

McAuliffe

Peachey

Turner

Johnson

About the Author

In 30 years as a writer, **Leo W. Banks** has published stories in the *Los Angeles Times Magazine*, *National Geographic Traveler*, *The Wall Street Journal*, *Sports Illustrated*, *The Boston Globe*, and numerous other publications. Since 1988, he has written 320 stories for *Arizona Highways* magazine, as well as five books. These include: *Double Cross: Treachery in the Apache Wars*; *Rattlesnake Blues: Dispatches From a Snakebit Territory*; *Manhunts and Massacres*; *Stalwart Women: Frontier Stories of Indomitable Spirit*; and *Never Stand Between a Cowboy and His Spittoon*. He also co-wrote *Travel Arizona II: A Guide to the Best Tours and Sites* and *Grand Canyon Stories: Then and Now*. He lives in Tucson.

Technical Reviewers

The author and *Arizona Highways* greatly acknowledge the assistance of four saguaro experts who reviewed the text to ensure technical accuracy.

Dr. Joe McAuliffe has conducted ecological research in the deserts of the American Southwest since 1981 and has written more than 35 research publications describing this work. In 1995, he received the W.S. Cooper Award from the Ecological Society of America for his research in the Sonoran Desert. He has served on the faculties of the University of Arizona and the University of Nevada, Las Vegas, where he taught courses on biology, ecology, and natural history of the desert Southwest. Since 1990, he has been the research ecologist and director of research at the Desert Botanical Garden in Phoenix.

Bill Peachey, a lifelong Arizonan raised in Phoenix, is a self-described science geek. As a boy he earned money by providing scorpions, at 5 cents apiece, to a doctor developing a scorpion antivenin. In addition to operating a saguaro study plot near Tucson's Colossal Cave Mountain Park, where he is park scientist, he has studied the paleoecology of sequoia redwoods in California and taught ecology at the Biosphere 2 north of Tucson. He also contributed a chapter on the caves of Arizona for a book by the National Speleological Society.

Born in Utah in 1927, **Raymond M. Turner**, a retired botanist for the United States Geological Survey, started his first saguaro study plot in 1959. He is the principal author of *Sonoran Desert Plants, an Ecological Atlas*, published in 1995. Turner co-authored the book *The Changing Mile*, matching contemporary and historic photos of the same landscapes from southern Utah to Guaymas, Mexico, and he and three others published an update, called *The Changing Mile Revisited*, in 2003. He returned to that theme in 2007 with the publication of *Ribbon of Green*, showing before and after photos of riparian habitats.

Matt Johnson has worked as manager and curator of the Desert Legume Program at the University of Arizona since 1990. The program, a joint project of the UA's College of Agriculture and Life Sciences and the Boyce Thompson Arboretum near Superior, is developing a comprehensive seed bank of wild species of legumes from dry regions around the world. He has written two books and more than 50 articles on the botany and horticulture of dry-climate plants.

Index

LEFT Protected by a large paloverde tree, this saguaro cactus is off to a healthy start in the Organ Pipe Cactus National Monument. David Elms, Jr.

Early morning sun warms a stand of saguaro cactuses in the Cholla Pass region of the Cabeza Prieta National Wildlife Refuge in southwestern Arizona. Randy Prentice